Enid Blyton's
NODDY
and the Difficult Day

BBC CHILDREN'S BOOKS

It was a busy, hustling, bustling day in Toyland. Everybody had lots of things to do and Noddy felt he had more to do than anybody.

Noddy dodged through the market square as fast as he could.

"Are you very busy, Noddy?" asked Dinah Doll.

"Yes," replied Noddy. "I have to collect some fish for Miss Pink Cat's supper party and fetch some hay for the animals at Mr and Mrs Noah's Ark."

"Would you have time to collect a box for me from the station?" Dinah Doll asked. "It's my new kitchen stool."

"I always find time for your errands, Dinah," said Noddy.

Noddy drove straight to the station. Bert Monkey was standing at the station entrance trying to hide something behind his back.

"Hullo, Bert Monkey," cried Noddy. "Have you seen a box?"

"No, I don't think I have," replied Bert Monkey, looking rather shifty.

"What's that behind your back?" asked Noddy, suspiciously.

"Er . . . I'm sure it's not a box," said Bert.

"Bert Monkey! Step aside!" ordered Noddy.

Bert Monkey came towards Noddy, but then turned round so that his tail covered Noddy's eyes.

"Stop that, you silly tail," exclaimed Noddy, pushing it away.

Noddy went up to the box and looked at it. It was for Dinah Doll.

"If you put that box in your car there won't be room for me and I *do* want a lift. I'm so tired and hungry," wailed Bert Monkey.

"There will be room for you, Bert, if you help me carry the box to my car and hold it very tightly as we go along," Noddy told him.

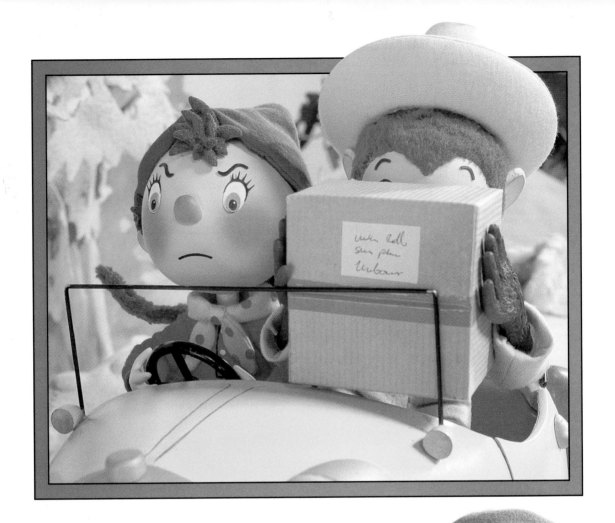

As Noddy drove along, Bert's
tail curled itself round Noddy's
shoulder. Then it knocked
Noddy's hat over his eyes.

"Help!" cried Noddy. "I can't
see!"

The car swerved and stopped so suddenly that the box flew out of Bert's hands. It went up into the air and landed on the ground with a crash.

"Look! Dinah's stool is broken!" said Noddy furiously. "Your tail is so naughty."

Noddy took the stool home and was trying to mend it when Master Tubby looked in.

"I'm very good at woodwork, Noddy," said Master Tubby, helpfully.

"Then mend this stool for me," said Noddy, "and I'll go and get you some lemonade."

But when Noddy came back he found that Master Tubby
had put the stool together all wrong.

"What have you done?" cried Noddy. "You've ruined
Dinah's stool."

"This is more interesting than a boring old stool!" said
Master Tubby, proudly.

"I shall just have to leave the stool till this evening," said
Noddy. "I've got all my other errands to do now."

At the harbour, Clockwork Clown was buying some fish from Sammy Sailor.

"There you are," cried Sammy Sailor, tossing a parcel to Clockwork Clown. "A lovely piece of cod."

"Thank you," said Clockwork Clown. "That should go down a treat!"

Then Noddy came along.

"I have to collect a special order for Miss Pink Cat," he told Sammy Sailor.

"This will be what you're after, young Noddy," said Sammy, handing him a parcel.

"At least *something* has gone right today," said Noddy.

As Noddy drove along he began to smell something horrible in his car.

"Ugh!" he said to himself. "It's coming from the parcel Sammy Sailor gave me."

Noddy stopped his car and opened the parcel. Inside he found some old fish bones.

"This can't be Miss Pink Cat's parcel," he cried in disgust. "It's just horrid old fish bones! But I can't go back now or I shall be too late to pick up the hay from the farm."

At the farm, smoke was pouring out of the barn. Mr and Mrs Straw were rushing to and from the duck pond with buckets of water.

"We must hurry, Mrs Straw," puffed Mr Straw. "We need more water to put out this fire!"

Just then, Noddy arrived. He looked very alarmed when he saw all the smoke.

"We've got a fire in our barn," explained Mrs Straw, anxiously.

"You must call the fire-engine!" cried Noddy.

"We have done," said Mrs Straw, "but it hasn't arrived yet."

"I'll help," said Noddy. "I'll go and fetch the fire-engine myself."

Noddy drove off and soon found Mr Sparks and his fire-engine standing in the road.

"What's wrong with your fire-engine?" Noddy called out. "It's needed at the farm."

"I can't make the engine work," said Mr Sparks, in despair.

"Leave this to me, Mr Sparks," said Noddy, importantly. "My car can tow your fire-engine!"

Noddy fixed a piece of strong rope to the back of his car
and tied the other end to the fire-engine. Then Noddy's little
car towed the fire-engine to the farm, with the bell ringing all
the way.

When they reached the farm,
Mr Sparks flew into action.

"Make way!" he shouted, as he
rushed along with his fire-hose.

"Well done, Noddy, for getting the fire-engine," said Mrs Straw. "But what's that terrible smell?"

Noddy explained about the smelly parcel of fish bones.

"Our pigs would like that," said Mrs Straw. "You can leave it with us."

"The fire's almost out," said Mr Sparks, "but I'll have to soak the rest of the hay in the barn to make sure it doesn't catch light again."

"Well, Noddy," said Mr Straw. "You won't be able to take this hay to the ark, I'm afraid."

"Oh, dear," said Noddy. "All my errands have gone wrong today."

"Don't worry, Noddy," said Mrs Straw. "We can give you some hay from our horse's stable."

"Yes," said Mr Straw. "I'm sure he won't mind."

Mrs Noah was very pleased with the hay
for her animals and she gave Noddy two sixpences.
"Don't worry about Miss Pink Cat's fish," she said.
"Our sea-lions have caught more fish today than they
need for their supper. You may take a couple."
"Oh, may I really?" said Noddy who was delighted.

Mr Noah threw the fish down to Noddy.

"Here you are, Noddy," he cried. "Catch!"

Noddy giggled and stood ready to catch the fish in his hat. "Thank you very much, Mr Noah," he shouted back.

Noddy drove straight to Miss Pink Cat's house.

"Hello, Miss Pink Cat," he called out, cheerfully. "I've brought your fish."

"In another minute you would have been late, Noddy, and then I would have been cross and told you off," said Pink Cat.

Miss Pink Cat took the fish and handed over a sixpence. Suddenly, Noddy noticed a yellow stool at Pink Cat's feet.

"Are you throwing that out?" he asked.

"Yes," said Pink Cat. "I don't want it any longer."

Noddy asked if he could take it. Miss Pink Cat was happy to let him have it.

Noddy found Dinah Doll at the café having an ice-cream.

"I've got your stool," he told her.

"My word!" said Dinah. "It's very bright, isn't it?"

"Don't you like the stool?" asked Noddy.

"I love it," said Dinah Doll. "I shall give you two sixpences for fetching it."

Noddy was delighted. "Two more sixpences!" he exclaimed.

"Have you got time for an ice-cream?" asked Dinah.

"Yes," said Noddy leaning back in his chair. "I'm not doing anything else today!"

"Nothing at all?" asked Dinah in surprise.

"Well, if I don't *do* anything, nothing can go wrong, can it?" said Noddy, chuckling happily.

More delightful Noddy stories to read and favourite characters to collect

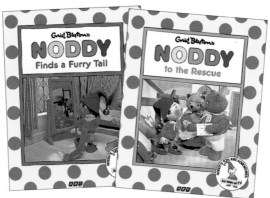

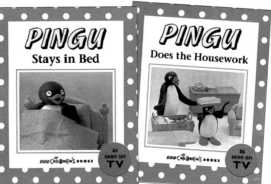

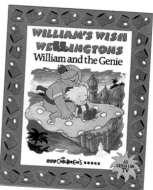

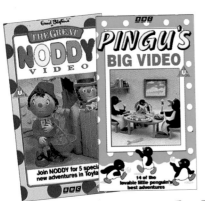

BBC CHiLDReN'S PUBLISHING